Give Us a Goal!

PAUL COOKSON

Illustrated by
DAVID PARKINS

F
FRANCES LINCOLN
CHILDREN'S BOOKS

CONTENTS

THE WARM-UP

FIRST HALF
PLAYING THE GAME

To Mark and Paul and

JANETTA OTTER-BARRY BOOKS

First published in Great Britain in 2004 by Macmillan Children's Books
This revised edition first published in 2012 by
Frances Lincoln Children's Books, 4 Torriano Mews,
Torriano Avenue, London NW5 2RZ
www.franceslincoln.com

*Don't Put Mum in Goals, Dad Said, Footy Look-a-Likes,
I Don't Want to Be in the Wall, My Great Gran The Football Fan,
L Plates on my Football Shirt, New Striker, Watching Football with
my Grandad, We Believe in Football, When Mum was the Trainer,
When the Wasp Flew up My Brother's Shorts* first published in 2012;
all other poems first published in 2004

A catalogue record for this book is available from the British Library.

ISBN 978-1-84780-341-2

Set in Cheltenham and Kosmik

Printed and bound by CPI Group (UK) Ltd, Croydon, CR0 4YY in June 2012

1 3 5 7 9 8 6 4 2

SECOND HALF
WATCHING THE MATCH

EXTRA TIME
MATCHES, PLAYERS

THE WARM-UP

The Footballer's Prayer

Our team
Which art eleven
Hallowed be thy game
Our match be won
Their score be none
On turf as we score at least seven
Give us today no daily red...card
And forgive us our lost passes
As we forgive those who lose passes against us
Lead us not into retaliation
And deliver us from penalties
For three is the kick off
The power and the scorer
For ever and ever
Full time

The Choosing

It's in the lap of the gods
Exactly who you are drawn to
The magical moment that decides
Whether you're red, white or blue
You don't choose the football team...
The football team chooses you

The highs, the lows, the thick and the thin,
Allegiance will always shine through
United you stand together forever
The heart forever is true
You don't choose the football team...
The football team chooses you

You are special, you are selected,
One of the chosen few
A bond that cannot be broken
There's nothing at all you can do
You don't choose the football team...
The football team chooses you.

Sonnet to the Team I Love

Shall I compare thee to a Saturday
Three o'clock the start in the afternoon
For then I watch my champions at play
Praying that we taste the victory soon
My heart beats wildly in my youthful breast
As we strive forward, onwards, evermore
Attack with vigour, vim and youthful zest
Perchance to shoot, perchance even to score
I swear allegiance to my belov'd team
Though days be dark and bleak as is the night
Perchance to wish, perchance even to dream
Of glories now within our mortal sight
   So long as men can breathe or eyes can see
   We will support the cause and follow thee.

Petrarchan Sonnet for The Team I Like the Least

With vengeance and with passion it is true
That there's a football team I love to hate
Whose skills and style I can't appreciate
Because they play in red shirts, not in blue
It's not just me, for thousands feel it too
Although their players may be good or great
It's natural for them to irritate
With arrogance and pride in all they do

I wish upon them losses and defeats
Though there be no logic to my reason
I pray they're thrashed and humiliated
Discontentment ever be their season
May their smug fans be squirming in their seats
Last not least, may they get relegated.

FIRST HALF
PLAYING THE GAME

When the Wasp Flew Up My Brother's Shorts

A family fun-filled holiday
Seaside football – match of the day
On the beach – the score nine nine –
When the match went into injury time
We soon forgot our day for sports
When the wasp flew up my brother's shorts

We misread the situation
Thought it was his celebration
Scoring a goal – dancing about
The yell, the scream, the twist and shout
We are all smiles as he cavorts
When the wasp flew up my brother's shorts

The moves he made – we'll never forget
The bottom wiggle and pirouette
The somersaults and acrobatics
A million amateur dramatics
Out of control and out of sorts
When the wasp flew up my brother's shorts

When the wasp flew up my brother's shorts
His eyes bulge wide and his face distorts
Worried where that wasp is caught
Scared of the sting, his body contorts
But the wasp was the one that was most distraught

Up one leg then down the other
Relief for the wasp, relief for my brother
Took them both a while to recover
Panic attacks and flash-back thoughts
When the wasp flew up my brother's shorts.

Don't Put Mum in Goals

She'll paint her nails and brush her hair
Can't decide just what to wear
Leave her handbags everywhere
Don't put Mum in goals

She might rip her mini skirt
She might get dirt on her new silk shirt
She might get hurt if she's not alert
Don't put Mum in goals

Stiletto heels aren't right at all
They might snap and then she'd fall
Even worse – they could burst the ball
Don't put Mum in goals

She might do all these and more
But there's one fact we can't ignore
She never, ever lets us score
Don't put Mum in goals

She dives and stretches, saves and stops
Keeps a clean sheet, calls the shots
Number one – she's the tops
That's why Mum's in goals

I Don't Want to Be in the Wall

There is nothing that is scarier
A free kick on the edge of the area
Ten yards back isn't far at all
I don't want to be in the wall

I don't want to feel that power
And blast at all those miles per hour
Faster than a cannonball
I don't want to be in the wall

Please don't hit me in the face
Or even worse - that lower place
So I crumble, scream and fall
I don't want to be in the wall

Wish I was – far too tall
Wish I was – far too small
Wish I wasn't scared of the ball
I don't want to be in the waaaaaaaaallllllllllll!

Family Footy Look-a-Likes

Grandad thinks he's Bobby Charlton just because he's
   bald
Uncle thinks he's Peter Crouch because he's really tall

Just because he wears a cap Dad thinks he's Petr Cech
Brother thinks he's Rooney because he looks like Shrek

When Mum Was the Trainer

Dad was really embarrassed
When Mum offered to be the trainer for his football team

She put perfume and bubble bath on the magic sponge
Gave everyone a nice cup of tea when they fell over

And when our tall, good-looking centre forward
Was tripped and fouled and hurt his knee

She took ever such a long time to rub it better
And then decided he needed the kiss of life

If I Was the England Manager

All opposition teams must wear pink.
And play in fluffy teddy-bear slippers and tutus.

Their goalposts must be twenty feet high
and thirty-five feet wide
while ours can be reduced and moved
at the touch of a remote-controlled button
in my tracksuit pocket.

Matches will finish when I decide it is appropriate,
but only when we have scored more goals and are winning.
So games could last for three hours, a week, a month
or the full-time whistle may be blown
after two minutes if we get an early break-through.

Floodlights can be angled and altered in such a way
that opposing goalkeepers are dazzled on high crosses.
Should that not work they can then be switched on and off
continuously until the desired effect is achieved.

In hot and humid matches
we are allowed to wear as much suntan cream as we want,
drink as much water and isotonic fluid as we want
and have a rest whenever we want.

The opposition, however, can only use cooking oil and
  Deep Heat
and must drink salt water and hot curried vegetable soup.

In cold and freezing conditions
we will wear our woolly gloves and hats,
thermal underwear and centrally heated shorts
but they must play in their pants and vests.
Or skins.

When we have a free kick defensive walls can stand within
  ten yards
although players are not allowed to protect themselves
  with their hands.

We must receive at least one penalty per game
while opposing goalkeepers are only allowed oven gloves
and a pair of horse's blinkers.

Our goalies meanwhile can utilise radar to detect
  dangerous crosses
and the liberal application of superglue.

World Cups will be ours,
the European Championships will be a formality
and record books will be rewritten forever
when I am the England Manager.

My Great Gran – The Football Fan

My great gran – the football fan
Watches me whenever she can
Never quiet – it's a riot
Always loud with my great gran

She knows the tactics, knows the plan
Shakes her head and waves her hand
Shouts advice that isn't nice
Take his legs! Mark your man!

Cross The Hulk with Desperate Dan
Frankenstein and Jackie Chan
No one's madder, no one's badder
Like an angry Superman

There's no one that's louder than
My great gran the football fan
She disagrees with referees
And now she has a touchline ban.

L Plates on my Football Shirt

When I play football for the football team at school
No one takes me seriously, they think I'm just a fool
My right boot's on my left foot, my left is on my right
My socks are on my arms and my shorts are far too tight

I've shin pads on my chin – because I cannot spell
My shirt is inside-out and upside-down as well
The laces on my boots are nearly five miles long
I need two weeks before each match so I can put them on

They told me to play sweeper – I borrowed my mum's
    hoover
Swept up their forward's shorts with a brilliant
    manoeuvre
They asked about my shooting, how I could attack
I got out my rifle – but they made me put it back

I told them that my dribbling was the best they'd get
Then dribbled down their shirts and made them soaking
    wet
They asked me to play winger – I said Well, I can't fly
Well, mark your man instead – so I gave him two black
    eyes

26

"Free Kick" said the ref so I did and watched him fall
Nobody had told me I should have kicked the ball
In view of this the referee gave the other team the kick
I was told to build a wall – but couldn't find a brick

In the end there's only two positions I can play
Left back, right back in the changing rooms all day
I'm only a beginner and someone could get hurt
So I don't have a number – but an L plate on my shirt

He Just Can't Kick it with his Foot

John from our team
Is a goal-scoring machine
Phenomenally mesmerizing but...
The sport is called football
But his boots don't play at all
Cos he just can't kick it with his foot.

He can skim it from his shin
He can spin it on his chin
He can nod it in the net with his nut
He can blow it with his lips
Or skip it off his hips
But he just can't kick it with his foot.

With simplicity and ease
He can use his knobbly knees
To blast it past the keeper, both eyes shut
He can whip it up and flick it
Up with his tongue and lick it
But he just can't kick it with his foot.

Overshadowing the best
With the power from his chest
Like a rocket from a socket he can put
The ball into the sack
With a scorcher from his back
But he just can't kick it with his foot.

Baffling belief
With the ball between his teeth
He can dribble his way out of any rut
Hypnotise it with his eyes
Keep it up on both his thighs
But he just can't kick it with his foot.

FLUMP!

BOBBLE

From his shoulder to his nose
He can juggle it and pose
With precision and incision he can cut
Defences straight in half
With a volley from his calf
But he just can't kick it with his foot.

He can keep it off the deck
Bounce the ball upon his neck
With his ball control you should see him strut
He can flap it with both ears
To loud applause and cheers
But he just can't kick it with his foot.

He can trap it with his tum
Direct it with his bum
Deflect it just by wobbling his gut
When he's feeling silly
He can even use his... ankle
But he just can't kick it with his foot.

31

Cool-Scorin' Match-Winnin' Celebratin' Striker

He's a shirt removin' crowd salutin'
handstandin' happy landin'
rockin' rollin' divin' slidin'
posin' poutin' loud shoutin'
pistol packin' smoke blowin'
flag wavin' kiss throwin'
hip swingin' arm wavin'
breakdancin' cool ravin'
shoulder shruggin' team huggin'
hot shootin' rootin' tootin'
somersaultin' fence vaultin'
last minute goal grinnin'
shimmy shootin' shin spinnin'
celebratin' cup-winnin' STRIKER!

33

No One Passes Me

I'm a blaster not a tapper
A ninety-minute scrapper
A chopper and a hacker
No one passes me

I've got the brawn and muscle
For the tackle and the tussle
I will hassle and I'll hustle
No one passes me

Harum-scarum do or dare 'em
I will take the knocks and bare 'em
Show me strikers and I'll scare 'em
No one passes me

I'm a winner not a loser
A rough 'em tough 'em bruiser
A goal scorer's confuser
No one passes me

Summer sun or winter mire
Lion hearted do or die-er
In my belly burns a fire
No one passes me

I'm a last-ditch tackle fighter
A knee and ankle biter
Nobody marks you tighter
Cos NO ONE passes me.

Proud Enough to Burst

When I scored my first goal
for the school team
I felt so proud inside
that I thought it would bubble up
and I would burst
even though we lost five one.

Twenty Things Needed for a Game of Football in the Local Park

1 Even number of players with at least four wearing anoraks or duffel coats.

2 Remove anoraks or duffel coats to use as goalposts.

3 Pick teams.

4 Do not pick smallest or fattest ones last.

5 Get out ball.

6 Argue with each other as to whose turn it was to bring ball.

7 Borrow friend's bike to go home and fetch ball.

8 Meanwhile, practise the art of spitting and clearing the nose.

9 Get out ball.

10 Argue with person who brought the ball as to why it is flat.

11 Borrow another friend's bike to fetch a pump and adaptor.

12 Meanwhile practise rude words to shout at non-existent referee.

13 Pump up ball.

14 Kick off and start game.

15 Commentate like John Motson on passing movements and eventual shot.

16 Argue whether shot
a) missed
b) went in
c) went over the anorak post
d) would have hit post and either gone in or bounced out.

17 Try to retrieve ball from muddy ditch behind goals.

18 Do not head ball for at least fifteen minutes

19 Get jeans as dirty as possible because the dirtier they are the better you must have played

20 Play until
a) everyone goes home
b) it is too dark to see
c) you are winning
d) you are winning, it is too dark to see and it is your ball anyway so you're going home anyway so there.

Dad Said

Dad said
He could beat us – blindfolded
With one leg tied behind his back

He was wrong

We ran rings around him
And beat him ten – nine
After extra time

New Striker

Our team has a brand new striker from abroad

Sergei
Sergei Callifragilistickexpialidocious

I like him so much
Dad bought me a shirt that had his name on the back

And on the front
And down both arms
And on the shorts as well

My Granny Could Score That...

It was easier to score
Couldn't hit a barn door
What was he aiming for?
What's he playing at?
One on one at last he's through
What on earth's he trying to do?
Missed it by a mile or two
My granny could score that!
And so could next door's cat!

How d'you miss an open goal?
He had time to take a stroll
Do you call that ball control?
What's he playing at?
How much are we paying him?
Anyone could knock it in
Does he really want to win?
My granny could score that!
And so could next door's cat!

My granny's got a Zimmer frame
But she'd play better in this game
She has glasses but she'd aim to get it in the net no sweat
Next door's cat is old and past-it
Always dozing in his basket
Even he could try and blast it in an open net, you bet.

It was easier to score
Couldn't hit a barn door
Missed a sitter once more
He needs looking at
If he can't see straight when he shoots
It's time to use the substitutes
They've both got their shooting boots
Granny and the cat,
They can't do worse than that!

My granny could score that!
And so could next door's cat!

Penalties

straightatthegoalie

what a save by the keep er

the keeper almost saved it

tripped up before I got to the ball

Poetry in Motion

Scorer, striker, artist, entertainer
Special skill standard maintainer
Never boring or mundaner
Highest quality campaigner

Turns on a sixpence
Predatory instincts
Measures any distance
In an instant

Lithe and lean – very acrobatical
A brain for the angles – very mathematical
Regal, royal – aristocratical
Theatrical – very dramatical
Standing ovations – the fans are fanatical

Show me a pair of heels that are cleaner
Or a physique that is leaner
Or a hunger that is keener
Or a finishing touch that's meaner
The grace and poise of a ballerina

Brain of a thinker, balance of a dancer
Ask him a question he's always got an answer
Every opportunity, every half chancer
Can he snap it up – of course he can sir...

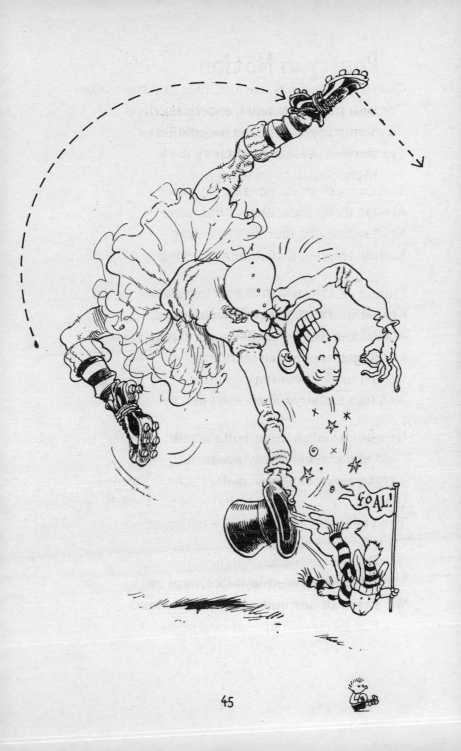

The jinks, the dinks, the dribbles and the tricks
The deft backheels and the delicate flicks
The punishing power, the bicycle kicks
The perfect placement slickety slick

Through defences, ghostly, haunting
Always dangerous, always daunting
Skill and ability, flair he's flaunting
Easing, teasing, testing and taunting

Pulling all the strings like a classical musician
Knows every trick just like a magician
Makes you feel better like a good physician
Feel the zeal of a man with a mission
Genius in any position
And he's a star you can wish on

He's got a vision, clear and specific
Cold and clinical – very scientific
Takes every chance no matter how diffic –
Ult it is
The same res-
Ult it is

Man of the match – plays like a dream
We just wish he could play for our team.

Perfect

Perfect.
Innocuous at first,
The ball looping over,
No real danger, nothing much on.

But he saw it first,
Acting instinctively and swiftly,
Stretching every single muscle
To claim first touch, the decisive kick.

Couldn't have been placed better...
The unreachable arc of the ball
Spinning about the stranded guardian
In slow, slow, s l o o o w w w motion.

The billow of the net from the kiss of the ball,
Perfect.
Well it would have been
If it had been at the other end of the pitch.

Pie Queue Haiku

Sometimes the only

Thing to look forward to is

The pie at half-time

Team Talk

Kick'em – nudge'em
Foul'em – budge'em
Poke'em – nut'em
Belt'em – butt'em
Pull'em – push 'em
Tug'em – rush'em
Trick'em – trip'em
Slide'em – slip'em
Charge'em – barge'em – chop'em – cheat'em
Doesn't matter how we beat'em

Not the actual words he said
But it was evident
The way he shook his fists and head
We all knew just what he meant

SECOND HALF
WATCHING THE GAME

Poem for the First Day of the Football Season

Brand-new start,
Last season is history and meaningless

My team has no points
And neither has yours.

All things are possible
And all glory dreamable.

Everything is winnable.
Potential is unmissable.

The peak of faith is scaleable.
The mountain of hope is touchable.
The summit of belief, believable.

Ten to three on that first Saturday
And nothing dulls the taste.

Excitement and anticipation
Tangible and tasteable.

Unparalleled success attainable.
This could be the best season of our lives.

Introducing Some Of The Team

Dave Tanka

Built like a rhino
Lumbering and cumbersome
But dependable
Solid, no quarter given
Always scores his penalties

Jamie Clerihew

Midfield dynamo, never thwarted
Plays for the team he's always supported
Always true blue through and through
Our very own Jamie Clerihew

Big Lee Merick

A tower of strength in each game
A powerful gigantic frame
Mean, moody, colossal
Of menace and muscle
A triumph of brawn over brain.

Tommy Coupletsen

Shining pate a-gleaming, mad eye crazy stare
Gritted teeth, determined, concentrated glare

Like a pirate on the seas ready for the plunder
Swashbuckling defences, tearing form asunder

Sharp and swift, decisive, committed to the cause
Mad Marauding Tommy deserving our applause

Werewolf Dad

Werewolf dad,
It's not a full moon once a month
But a home match every two weeks.

He gradually changes,
Once inside the ground he fidgets and twitches,
Dribbles on his scarf and pie.

Just before kick-off
The veins on his neck stand out
And he bounces up and down on the spot.

It's three o'clock and the change is complete,
The whistle blows and that's it...
Howling and barking at the men in the middle.

Mild-mannered dad
To mad werewolf football fan
In ninety minutes plus injury time.

Dad Don't Shout At the Ref!

Always just the same, every single game
I bet that you can hear him in Kiev
Does he have to be so loud? He's louder than the crowd
Dad – don't shout at the ref!

His cheeks are burning red, each hair stands off his head
Raving without even taking breath
Yelling and he's screaming and both his ears are steaming
Dad – don't shout at the ref!

There's no chance of him stopping, both his eyes are
    popping
Cursing like a foul-mouthed TV chef
Jumping when he rants like there's scorpions down his
    pants
Dad – don't shout at the ref!

Always disagreeing with everything he's seeing
Every little thing leaves him bereft
Sweating most profusely while his tongue is wagging
    loosely
Dad – don't shout at the ref!

Do you know the rules? You silly stupid fool
Are you blind as well as dumb and deaf?
Holding up his glasses every time he passes
Dad – don't shout at the ref!

That was never yellow, you stupid little fellow
Raging like a banshee in Macbeth
Can you call this sport, the way his face contorts?
Dad – don't shout at the ref!

His theory seems to be, it's a conspiracy,
Complaining that it might as well be theft
Screaming and howling that no one sees the fouling
Dad – don't shout at the ref!

Because he's inconsistent, berating the assistant
That a fate awaits them both that's worse than death
We know his football passion'll make him more irrational
Dad – don't shout at the ref!

Mum's partly to blame when she says *it's just a game*
And asks him whether all his sense has left
If he doesn't start to stop it then his heart is going to cop it
Dad – don't shout
Don't let your anger out
It's not what it's about…
DAD – DON'T SHOUT AT THE REF!

Of Course I Could Be Wrong

Warm-up matches have all gone well
The strikers are on song
Lots of goals, it's looking good
This year could be the best for years
Of course...I could be wrong.

New players passing, gelling well
A sense they all belong
It bodes well for the future
This year could be the best for years
Of course...I could be wrong.

Fresh purpose and fresh vigour
To carry us along
They seem to be attacking more
This year could be the best for years
Of course...I could be wrong.

Young stars are on the verge
Confidence is strong
Everybody's positive
This year could be the best for years
Of course...I could be wrong.

Happy days could soon be here
The wait's been far too long
It's best not to count chickens
This year could be the best for years
Of course...I could be wrong.

Again

Success could be a word that rolls
Off everybody's tongue
This could be a new era
This year could be the best for years
Let's prove the others wrong.

Elevens

Poems that use eleven words only and reflect football team formations.

If we all stand on the line perhaps they won't score

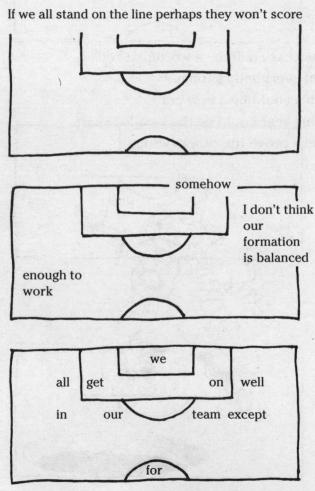

somehow

I don't think
our
formation
is balanced

enough to
work

we

all get   on   well

in   our   team except

for

him

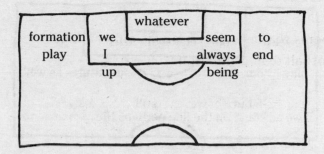

formation | we | whatever | seem | to
play | I | | always | end
| up | | being

substitute

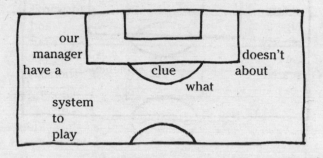

our
manager | | | doesn't
have a | | clue | about
| | what
system
to
play

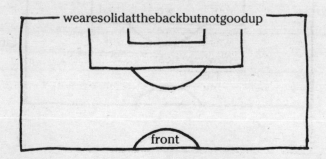

wearesolidatthebackbutnotgoodup

front

week our manager tried to

play our five substitutes as well

but we still lost

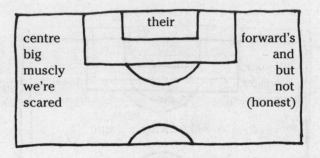

centre forward's
big and
muscly but
we're not
scared (honest)

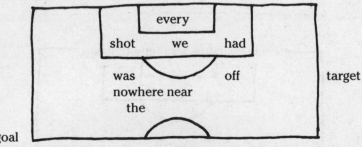

every

shot we had

was off target

nowhere near

the

goal

64

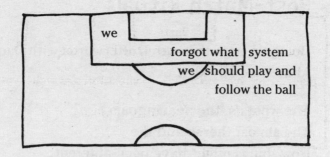

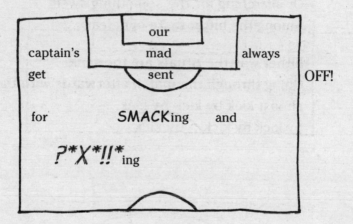

Post-Match Rituals

Going through the match afterwards with Dad,
Almost kick by kick.

The what ifs, the nearly goals,
The almost theres and the
How things might have been different.

Savouring the glorious flavours of victory
Or searching for the something sweet
Among the bitter taste of defeat.

Either way the rituals are the same
Going through the match afterwards with Dad,
almost kick by kick by kick...
by kick by kick... by kick....

Watching Football with my Grandad

Watching football with my grandad
Feels like school and history
He tells me of the good old days
And the way things used to be

Way back when – men were men
Shoulder barges were allowed
No one minded proper tackles
No one dived and rolled around

Nobody wore gloves in Winter
No one swore and no one spat
No one kissed when goals were scored
They shook hands and that was that

Proper footballs with pig's bladders
Real footballs, real leather
Head it and you'd get a headache
Like a stone in wetter weather

Everybody's hair was short
No ear rings and no tattoos
Nobody earned stupid money
The game was only back page news

Saturdays were football days
Every kick-off was at three
Proper football, says my grandad
Football like it used to be

Haikus

The crowd is full of
Fat men in replica shirts
Wishing they were stars

Shouting loud advice
On how to play the game when
They can't play themselves

Mr Kenning – The Referee

Match starter
Watch watcher
Time keeper
Play stopper

Decision maker
Foul ignorer
Blind eye-er
Game changer

Headline causer
Finger pointer
Penalty giver
Card waver

Crowd incensor
Hassle taker
Abuse listener
No mate-er

Hot seater
Black wearer
Gun sticker
Whistle blower

A.C. Rostic — Goalkeeper

Gargantuan, colossus, somewhat god-like
Omnipresent guardian of the goals
A giant among mortals, superhuman
Lord of the area he patrols
Keeper of the nets, he keeps them empty
Everything he touches he controls
Even shots of thunder and deflections
Perfect timing, joyous to behold
Ever the invincible of athletes
Reflexes of lightning, touch of gold

Wow!

First Half . . .

The atmosphere's electric at
The all engrossing action packed
All absorbing captivating rip roaring fascinating
Heady and intoxicating fever pitch exhilarating
Pulse quickening adrenaline pumping
Senses reeling heartbeat thumping
End to end and inspired
Rock and roller coaster ride

Second Half . . .

It's a topsy turvy give and take
Hundred mile an hour rate
Spell binding hypnotic
Kamikaze chaotic
Thrills, spills, incident filled
Special and sensational
Enthralling inspirational
Nerve shredding mind blowing
Total draining never slowing
Enthusiastic most fantastic
Football match you've ever been at
You can't take your eyes off the action for a minute
Never has ninety minutes had so much packed in it.

Full Time

Chants That Didn't Catch On

Who's the nice man in the black?
We all love the referee!
His eyesight's always perfect!
Yes we all agree-ee!

Offside! Never mind!
2-4-6-8! the other team is really great!
Yes it was a very good goal
Even though it was against us!

Ooh we like the colours on your shirts!
We lost but you played well!
We shared all the pies!
Nil nil! Nil nil! Nil nil! Nil nil!

See you at the next match then!
Ooh ah Ooh ah! Oh what sporting fans you are!
Wemberlee! Wemberlee! It's a stadium in London
and they call it Wemberlee!
And you'll never walk alone — especially when our
coach can give you a lift home!

Five Radio Lives

Listening to the match on the radio
Is not good when the reception is bad
As it often *cracklescracklesfizzzzzcrackles*
And fades out at fizz most import*crackle*fizztant *crackle*
      mo*crackle*ment

      When the commentary match is not my team's
      My heart is in my mouth
      Wherever they break to go to our match
      As they only report when a goal is scored
      And my heart skips a beat, hoping that it's ours.

      When it's not, it's horrible,
      Especially when the same thing happens
      Again
      Ten minutes later
      And then again.

I hate not seeing the pictures and what's happening
But I love the excitement
When I can hear the roar of the crowd
And the commentators go absolutely wild.

Sometimes I get so mad when we are losing
That I switch off in anger and stomp about
Only to switch it back on again
Straight away
Just in case things have changed.

A goal is a goal is a goal.
Even when I'm alone in my room
With only a radio
A goal is a goal is a goal
And always something to celebrate.

Dear Referee

I saw you when you fell and slipped
Upon the greasy mud and tripped

You slid headfirst along the grass
And dirt at speeds none can surpass

Smeared head to toe in slime and mud
We've never seen refs look so good

The fans united in their cheers
The funniest thing we've seen for years

Your antics brightened up the gloom
Best thing you did all afternoon

It made me laugh and made my day
The match was boring anyway.

Signed and meant, sincerely yours
For once deserving of applause.

Come back soon and may I quip
I hope that you enjoyed your trip

It couldn't happen to a better man
So here's to next time,
                              A football fan.

Just One of Those Games

Every little touch and trick was magic
Everything he touched just turned to dust
Every single pass reached its target
Ballooning passes straight up to the touch
Every tackle total and well-timed
Tackles later than a much-delayed train
Every fifty-fifty ball was his
Slipped and fell then slipped and fell again
Quick-thinking, speedy, fleet of foot
Cumbersome and seemed to wade in honey
Right place, right time, right direction
Wrong, wrong, wrong but always funny
Majestic in the air for every high ball
Concussed and banged his goalie on the head
Every shot he had went on target
Either his own players or Row Zed
Almost telepathic with his team mates
Couldn't find his own team with a map
Timed his runs to absolute perfection
Always caught out by the offside trap
Scored a hat trick of the highest calibre
Couldn't hit a barn door with a banjo
Hit the woodwork twice and won a penalty
To cap it all he scored a great own goal
Everything just worked, he didn't put a foot wrong

Nothing could be worse, couldn't do a thing right
On top of his game and really on song
He couldn't have changed if he'd played all night
Dazzling, brilliant, a blinder, on fire
A stinker, a horror, a nightmare that's rotten
A match to be remembered forever
A match to be forgotten!

Everybody's different, no one is the same
Good or bad, just one of those games.

That Sinking Feeling

It's that sinking feeling
In the pit of your stomach,
The lump in the throat,
That numbness and nothingness
When you've watched your favourite football team lose.
They had the chances but couldn't score.
They gave away an easy goal.
They didn't play as well as they did in the last match.

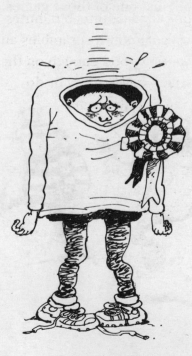

It's that sinking feeling
When you feel like shutting yourself away
Until all your best friends forget the score.
But they never do
And they take every opportunity
To remind you in great and fondest detail
With their slow motion replay commentary.

It's that sinking feeling
When despite the last fifteen minutes of pressure,
Near misses, goalmouth scrambles and amazing saves
They just weren't good enough on the day
And no matter what you say or do
The score remains the same.
It's that sinking feeling
When the most you can hope for
Is that your best friend's favourite team
Lost by more goals than yours.

Fortune Favours the Brave

Fortune favours the brave
A smash and grab goal and penalty save
A brilliant stop and the crowd forgave
This week's hero, last week's knave
It may have been a close close shave
Thanks to the woodwork we can crave
All three points and shout and wave
We can chant and we can rave
Fortune favours the brave.

The Weather, the Winning and the Losing

On those days when we win
The bad weather doesn't matter one bit
But on those days when we don't
Every raindrop pummels home the defeat,
Every ice-blast of wind chills the weary bones,
Every snowflake in the eyes freezes frustration's tears
And the longing for home and a hot drink increases
     infinitely.

The cold feels colder
The wet feels wetter
Everything's worse
Nothing's better
But on the days that we win
Nothing else matters.

Goal of the Season

Unstoppable – a belter
A real goal-net melter

Unreachable – a stinger
A sizzling humdinger

Unsaveable – a blaster
A hundred mile right past you

Untouchable – a screamer
A centre forward's dream-er

Unforgettable – a scorcher
A form of goalie torture

Unrepeatable – a winner
A never quite the same again-er

Unique – the reason
The goal of the season

The Football Results are as Follows

The Football Results are as Follows

The game was	1	derful hope you enjoyed it	2
I don't know if	5	ever seen a better match be	4
Now I'm feelin'	0	not just because of the pie I	8
Scoring that many's	7	but hell for them because we	1
At least we reached our po	10	tial with our talented first	11
All their supporters are	6	as parrots they just couldn't go	1
Playing with total	3	dom we will always domin	8
It was our vir	2	uoso performance they just	
		couldn't sur	5

Poem for the Last Day of the Season

It looked so good
Halfway through
Unfulfilled
Potential blue

Early exits
From each cup
Safe and sound
But not quite up

We could have done
So much more
Lost too many
Couldn't score

Signs of hope
With good reason
Same time same place
Next football season

EXTRA TIME
MATCHES AND PLAYERS

Magic and Loss

The magic of the FA Cup
The giant killing dream
Everyone wants an upset but
Not against their team

The romance of the fight
The tie that steals the scene
Everyone wants an upset but
Not against their team

The struggle and the glory
The drama of the story
It's all in ninety minutes
A bit of luck could win it
Eleven v. eleven
Dreams of cup tie heaven
It's a level field of play
It's all about the day

The magic of the FA Cup
The giant killing dream
Everyone wants an upset but
Not against their team

Savour the Flavour

Savour the flavour – the taste of success
The singing, the grinning when we are the best
The smiles last for miles outshining the rest
We savour the flavour – the taste of success

The joy in the joining of sweet celebration
The victory chants, the songs of elation
Losing ourselves in complete jubilation
The joy in the joining of sweet celebration

We're winners, we're victors, we've beaten the rest
The FA Cup Final, the best of the best
Flying our colours we've passed every test
We savour the flavour – the taste of success.

Germany 1 England 5

Once every so often it happens.
It feels like it's never going to happen
and sometime it doesn't
but once every so often it actually happens.

Once every so often
you see a football match so special
that it becomes part of the national heritage,
a match that takes on legendary status,
folklore and glory.

Dads and grandads have had their 1966,
Hurst, Moore, Peters, Charlton, Ball et al
England 4 West Germany 2.

Big brothers and uncles had 1996
trouncing Holland 4-1.

But what have we had?
Lost penalty shoot-outs, early exits
and never quite reaching any potential.

Until now . . .

We watched it, couldn't quite believe our eyes,
but we watched it, smiling, cheering, laughing, revelling
and we were part of the shared experience
of history in the making,
when fate conspires
to juggle all the variables in our favour
so that even when going 1-0 down
every chance is taken and we get to demolish Germany,
yes . . . demolish Germany 5-1.

To score five is remarkable.
To score five away from home is amazing.
To score five away from home against Germany
is not just remarkable and amazing but almost unreal.

Owen – three, a hat trick,
Gerrard and Heskey, one apiece.
History, real history
and even while the teams still played
we knew then that this was the match we had been
    waiting for – for so, so long,
that this match was indeed history in the making,
a match to remember.

Our match to remember.

Tonight I Played Like Beckham, Today He Played Like Me

England 2 – Greece 2

Tonight I played like Beckham,
today he played like me.
True, I haven't got the skill
and I can't bend it like him.
OK, I didn't score the free kick against Greece
that took us to the World Cup –
mine went over the hedge into next door's greenhouse –
but tonight I played like Beckham,
and today he played like me.

It wasn't anything to do with ability
but everything to do with attitude.
He was like a kid in the park,
anoraks for goalposts,
wanting to kick every single ball,
be involved in every single move,
tackle every single tackle.
His position went out of the window,
he was everywhere,
left, right, centre, attack and defence,
like a bee around the honey pot.

And it was because of that,
because he was once again that kid in the park
who'll play till it's dark,
that kid who'll carry on
because he doesn't want to lose,
that tonight I played a little bit like Beckham
and today he played a little bit like me.

Except he was better.

We Believe in Football

A ninety minute drama
Each story yet untold
The tension, twists and turns
We watch it all unfold
The heroes and the villains
The tears and the laughter
But no one guarantees
A happy ever after.

The past is always with us
Those ties we cannot sever
The triumphs and the tragedies
That bring us all together
The legacy of legends
Both on and off the pitch
We all know our history
Munich, Hillsborough, Sixty Six.

The deftness and the touches
The balance and control
Telepathic vision
The special wonder goal
The something out of nothings
These mesmerising tricks
We practise in the playground
What's perfect on the pitch.

Artisans and artists
Creative and instinctive
Old masters and young mavericks

Style and poise distinctive
Admired time and time again
We marvel at the art of it
Each picture tells a story
So glad we are a part of it.

We believe in hope
We believe in dreams
Anything is possible
The future yet unseen
On any given match day
Eleven vee eleven
We could punch above our weight
Be in football heaven.

Be it baggy shirts and brylcreem
A mullet or moustache
Football equals stylishness
Each little touch of class
This game that we call beautiful
The craft, technique and guile
Whatever the result
Let's win or lose in style.

The passion on the pitch
The passion in the stands
The importance of our earnestness
Right across this land
Nine, nineteen or ninety nine
We still have that dream
To score the winning goal
For our favourite football team.

Paul Cookson has been a football fan longer than he has been a poet. Since 2004 he has worked with the National Football Museum as their official Poet in Residence. He has also worked with Liverpool Libraries as Poet for the Everton Collection and his football poems have featured on Match of the Day and various national radio stations. He has held the World Cup and met six of the World Cup Winners from 1966.

As a poet, Paul has over 40 titles to his name and his poems have appeared in over two hundred collections. He spends most of his time visiting schools and festivals, performing his work and leading workshops.

Now that he's over 50 Paul should have retired from 5-a-side football – but he hasn't.

www.paulcooksonpoet.co.uk